FIRST STORY

First Story changes lives through writing.

We believe that writing can transform lives, and that there is dignity and power in every young person's story.

First Story brings talented, professional writers into secondary schools serving low-income communities to work with teachers and students to foster creativity and communication skills. By helping students find their voices through intensive, fun programmes, First Story raises aspirations and gives students the skills and confidence to achieve them.

For more information and details of how to support First Story, see www.firststory.org.uk or contact us at info@firststory.org.uk.

Mirrors in the Circus
ISBN 978-0-85748-296-9

Published by First Story Limited
www.firststory.org.uk
Omnibus Business Centre,
39–41 North Road
London
N7 9DP

Typesetting: Avon DataSet Ltd
Cover Designer: Dipa Mistry
Printed in the UK by Aquatint

First Story is a registered charity number 1122939 and a private company limited by guarantee
incorporated in England with number 06487410. First Story is a business name of First Story Limited.

Mirrors
in the Circus

An Anthology

BY THE FIRST STORY GROUP
AT NOTTINGHAM ACADEMY RANSOM ROAD CAMPUS

EDITED AND INTRODUCED BY MARK GWYNNE JONES | 2018

FIRST STORY

Changing lives through writing

'We all have a voice. Some never discover it. We all have stories to tell. Some never tell them. First Story has helped all these young writers to discover their writing voice, and in so doing has helped them discover themselves.'
Michael Morpurgo (author of *War Horse*)

'First Story is a fantastic idea. Creative writing can change people's lives: I've seen it happen. It's more than learning a skill. It's about learning that you, your family, your culture and your view of the world are rich and interesting and important, whoever you happen to be. Teenagers are under increasing pressure to tailor their work to exams, and to value themselves in terms of the results. First Story offers young people something else, a chance to find their voices.'
Mark Haddon (author of *The Curious Incident of the Dog in the Night-Time*)

'First Story not only does an invaluable thing for the young and under-heard people of England, it does it exceptionally well. Their books are expertly edited and beautifully produced. The students featured within are wonderfully open and candid about their lives, and this is a credit to First Story, whose teachers thoroughly respect, and profoundly amplify, their voices. The only problem with First Story is that they're not everywhere – yet. Every young person deserves the benefit of working with them.'
Dave Eggers (author of *A Heartbreaking Work of Staggering Genius*)

'First Story is an inspiring initiative. Having attended a school with a lot of talented kids who didn't always have the opportunity to express that talent, I know what it would have meant to us to have real-life writers dropping by and taking our stories seriously. And what an opportunity for writers, too, to meet some of the most creative and enthusiastic young people in this country! It's a joyful project that deserves as much support as we can give it.'
Zadie Smith (winner of the Orange Prize for fiction and author of *White Teeth*)

As Patron of First Story I am delighted that it continues to foster and inspire the creativity and talent of young people in secondary schools serving low-income communities.

I firmly believe that nurturing a passion for reading and writing is vital to the health of our country. I am therefore greatly encouraged to know that young people in this school – and across the country – have been meeting each week throughout the year in order to write together.

I send my warmest congratulations to everybody who is published in this anthology.

Camilla

HRH The Duchess of Cornwall

Thank You

Kate Kunac-Tabinor, **Lucy Cowdery**, **Chris Scotcher**, and all the designers at **OUP** for their overwhelming support for First Story, and **Dipa Mistry** specifically, for giving their time to design this anthology.

Melanie Curtis at **Avon DataSet** for her overwhelming support for First Story and for giving her time in typesetting this anthology.

Moya Birchall at **Aquatint** for printing this anthology at a discounted rate.

Open Gate Trust who supported First Story in this school.

HRH The Duchess of Cornwall, Patron of First Story.

Thanks to:
Arts Council England, Alice Jolly & Stephen Kinsella, Andrea Minton Beddoes & Simon Gray, The Anson Charitable Trust, The Arvon Foundation, BBC Children in Need, BBC Radio 4 Appeal & Listeners, Beth & Michele Colocci, Big Lottery Fund, Blackwells,

Boots Charitable Trust, Brunswick, Charlotte Hogg, Cheltenham Festivals, Clifford Chance, Danego Charitable Trust, First Editions Club Members, First Story Events Committee, Frontier Economics, Give A Book, Hollick Charitable Trust, Ink@84, Ivana Catovic of Modern Logophilia, Jane & Peter Aitken, John Lyon's Charity, John R Murray Charitable Trust, John Thaw Foundation, Lake House Charitable Foundation, Letters Live, Liz and Terry Bramall Foundation, Old Possum's Practical Trust, Open Gate Trust, Oxford University Press, Psycle Interactive, Robert Webb, Royal Society of Literature, Sigrid Rausing Trust, Sir Halley Stewart Trust, The Stonegarth Fund, Teach First, Tim Bevan & Amy Gadney, The Thomas Farr Charity, Walcot Foundation, Whitaker Charitable Trust, XL Catlin, our group of regular donors, and all those donors who have chosen to remain anonymous.

Most importantly we would like to thank the students, teachers and writers who have worked so hard to make First Story a success this year, as well as the many individuals and organisations (including those who we may have omitted to name) who have given their generous time, support and advice.

Contents

Introduction

Mark Gwynne Jones

The book you hold is a collection of poems and stories written over the course of nine months by students who volunteered their time to write. Here are the thoughts, hopes, dreams and anxieties of a culturally diverse group of students whose ages ranged from Year Seven to those sitting their GCSE's. From the point of view of facilitating the workshops, the age difference was a challenge but it also presented some wonderful opportunities. When some of the older students shared their rites of passage through startlingly insightful poems written there and then in the environment of a noisy classroom, it sent a visceral bolt of energy through all present. It made hairs stand up, bodies sit up and minds light up. And the creativity was contagious.

Whilst editing this anthology I kept reading poems that made me think 'I should quote that in the introduction' – only to realise the introduction would soon read like an amalgam of all the poems in the book. A super poem drawn from the raw emotions and insights of the bewildering, sometimes dangerous, passage of adolescence. A journey that's even more poignant when the world is in such flux. Here are poems tracing where these young people are *from*; outlining the things that make them who they are while acknowledging the mystery of existence: 'I come from a maths equation / that has never been discovered /... from a work of art / that has never been seen / I come from everywhere and nowhere / And I am special because / There's only one of me.' Here too are poems of love, death and desire whose stories are like fruits: 'They open up / So many new tastes.'

Perhaps the most rewarding development of my residency was how students who at first were reluctant to read or share their work — would later accost me as soon as I arrived, wanting to read aloud their latest creation. And it was at that point I realised they'd got the 'bug'. There's an inherent joy in being creative. It's an act of self-discovery that can be conducted no matter your circumstances. Even when denied paper and pen, people have composed and memorised whole collections of poems. Being creative is a lifelong means of discovery, and I believe many of the students who have contributed to this book recognise this and will continue to write and discover.

I would like to thank the group's English teacher, Miss Nina Green, for all her support, encouragement and ideas for writing (it is very apparent how much Miss Green is valued by her students, and for good reason). I'd also like to thank the Head of English, Mr Jamie Hall, for his continued enthusiasm and support for the project and for inviting me to burst into his classroom to read poems that September afternoon. I'd like to thank my shadow writer, Beth Fear, who joined in on the sessions, helped students with their writing and very kindly typed up some of their handwritten work. Thanks must also go to First Story's co-ordinator for the East Midlands, Jess Tickell, and to all the First Story team who have made my time at Nottingham Academy possible. And most of all, I'd like to thank the students who stayed behind on Thursday afternoons to sit in a circle and write, sharing with me all the things that make up this book and more — may they continue to express themselves with honesty and courage.

His Dark Eye...

Chloe Belshaw

His dark eye…
Staring at the ground.

His scars still bleeding…
He used to be a brave prince,

But now he is a slave.
His filthy hands
Touching the leaves, a feather
That fell,
On his knotted head.

The trees whisper.
Telling him secrets
He doesn't want to know.

But everyone knows him,
And his eye stays in the forest

Forever.

The Lightning Lit a Tragic Night

Chloe Belshaw

The lightning lit a tragic night,
Whistles of wind, banging on my shed.
My naughty neighbour
Moaning at me
Because my guinea pig died
On his dirty wet step.

Me and Lilly ran away.

Finally, we got home and then,
Knocking at my door,
In sprinkles of rain,
The soaked mail-man returned,
Delivering a parcel.

Heat Is on My Face

Chloe Belshaw

Heat is pressing down on my face.

Blood pressure's high,
Time is going backwards,
Sometimes fast, sometimes slow.

Perhaps it's normal.
As time flies, people change;
Life gets hard.
It's hard for me.
Getting grounded was a mistake,
All the trouble I made.

Why does time heat my face?

My Name Is

Chloe Belshaw

My name is Chloe, knowing Crazy starts with C.
The moving parts in my body,
Like a balloon in the sky, feeling I
Could crash one day.

The wind blows in my face,
Strong enough to push me back to the floor.
I'm just going crazy in a maze.
The lonely girl in the ripped dress.

Ripped like a curtain.

The darkness in a cave,
Crying for help
I'm sending myself in waves.

My name is Chloe, waving goodbye.

I Come From

Kiera Campbell

I come from a dream that's been lost forever.
I come from a strange life,
With my friends.
We all go off on our dreams
That have been lost forever.

I come from a family who are weird… kind… sweet…
They love me to pieces
But we all have our problems.

I come from a dream that's lost for all eternity.
No one will hear my voice 'til I die
Then you will hear me louder than you could before.

I come from a maths equation
That has never been discovered.
I come from a work of art
That has never been seen.

I come from everywhere and nowhere,
And I am special because
There is only one of me.

The Wind Is

Kiera Campbell

The wind is

Everywhere and nowhere.

It grabbed the hood of my coat

And dragged me backwards to the ground.

The wind stopped me in my tracks

And I could barely move.

The wind is too

Powerful.

The wind

Is.

Shadow of Death

Kiera Campbell

I guessed that something was wrong.
The stale smell of the old rug sent a shiver through my body.
It reminded me of my great nana.
I always knew we were close
But not this close.
If only I knew why she was here at the end of the hallway.
I love her so much, but she is scaring me now.
The last thing I wanted to do that day
Was to say goodbye to her.
I miss her so.
That fatal day, I watched from the shadows
As they shot her dead
And I fell to the ground and cried.

Death

Kamilė Ćerekavičiūtė

The start of the unknown, the end of your time on the throne.
But maybe the unknown is the so-called 'zone' where it's all
    you wanted in life.
It's life's big mystery that puts you out of your misery,
But what if this beauty is gone?

You become immortal, with no right to be moral.
The start, or the end?
Think quickly before your time's up, my friend.

And I Never Was That Drunk…

after M. Leknickas

Kamilė Ćerekavičiūtė

She was the falling star in the night sky.
She was the glistening light
Reflecting onto my wine glass.
She was the cigarette smoke
That my chapped lips blew out
When saying her name.
She was the newly-bloomed daisy
On my great-Grandfather's grave.
She was the smell
Of a freshly blown out candle.
No more, never less.

No

Kamilė Ćerekavičiūtė

I guessed something was wrong as soon as I said *No*.
As soon as I shouted *No!*
As soon as I screamed *Stop*
At the top of my lungs,
And it didn't stop.
And the feeling of weakness
Heavily weighted my chest.

The sounds of the environment suddenly blurred
And all I could hear was heavy breathing
And my own heartbeat echoing inside my ribcage.

All I could do was look at the handprint
On this bathroom's mirror
And wonder how long it had been there.
Just quietly hoping for it all to end.

It's ironic, isn't it?
How little girls are expected to wear skirts,
But now the case is closed after the words *she was asking for it*
    are spoken.

I Remember

Kamilė Ćerekavičiūtė

I remember when girls were considered beautiful without spending their lunch money on appetite suppressants.

I remember when girls were considered beautiful without pushing two fingers down their throat to cleanse from last night's dinner lies.

I remember when girls were considered beautiful without wearing tight miniskirts or shoes that give them blisters.

I remember when scarred wrists were something worth seeing a psychiatrist for, not the hottest trend you'd be a fool not to follow.

I remember when thigh-gaps were considered a sign of anorexia, not the new standard of beauty.

I remember when whole families were considered the norm, but it's become such an irregularity that kids have forgotten the definition of regular.

Fruits

Caitlyn Clegg

Trees produce many fruits:
Sour ones,
Sweet ones,
And some that are bitter.

Their fruits are like stories,
They open up
So many new tastes.
And oh how those tastes differ:
One person's sour is another's bitter.

A story is a juicy fruit
Born of a tree with branches and roots.

I Come From

Caitlyn Clegg

I come from a city
Filled with grey clouds and buildings
Which tower above me as I walk.

I come from a street
Where leaves cover the floor
And the freezing cold air makes your arms red.

I come from a family
Who scream at the TV
Whenever the football's on

And where 7pm is a time when family comes first.

I come from bedtime stories
With my mum, who sat with me in my bed
And drifted me to sleep with princesses and frogs.

I come from a school
Where education slowly drifts you to dreaming
And scary minds fill the buildings.

And lastly, I come from ink.
How it covered my arms
From blue to red,

I come from Nottingham.

The Classroom

Caitlyn Clegg

Insert knowledge here…
Insert the person typing in the background…
Insert the people chewing at the back…
The person at the front who likes attention…
Insert the person with all the questions…
Insert the gossip gals talking…
The bullies throwing paper aeroplanes…
Insert the people who are quote-un-quote 'emo'…
Insert the people who are actually depressed…
The teacher who tells you how to work…
Could you cope with all the noise?

My Name Is

Caitlyn Clegg

My name is Caitlyn
From the Irish: Kathlyn.
My name is blue,
Stemming cherry blossoms,
My name is Caitlyn.
It's a 'C' not a 'K'
A 'Y' not an 'I'.
My name
Is pure snow
On the ground
Making that crunch as you walk,
My name is Caitlyn.

New Eyes

Nicole Fontes

I received new eyes
And I saw my dad's face for the first time.
All the details in his face,
No clearer could they be
Now the gift of sight has been given to me.
The irises of his eyes are no longer a dull, tree-bark-brown,
But shimmering rays of green swim across their surface.
He no longer has old, porcelain skin;
With a freshly cut beard, my dad has freckles.
Baffled, I move on to other wonders
And through the window, farther than I could gaze before,
I see the tree has nearly as many branches
As I do locks on my head.
The flickering, wrinkled, condensation-touched leaves
Dance in the wind.
Wind so clear I can nearly see it.
I can *see* the wind.
I bet you can't.
I wish you could though.
A gift so precious, I wish I could share it.
My first adventure with new eyes,
As grateful as I am, I am now overwhelmed.
I shall put them to rest. There's always tomorrow.
God bless you for my eyes.

Daily Nothing of an Old Couple

Nicole Fontes

An old lady on her way to the shop
Stopped in the middle of the road when she felt a little raindrop,
Worrying a storm was coming
The silly old lady was left squirming.

All the way back on Maine Street at the old lady's house
Her husband sat on the floor playing with a dirty kitchen mouse,
Squeak... Squeak... said Mr Thomas
Here she comes back with two llamas.

Oh Mildred, you silly old hag,
Instead of buying llamas you should have stopped by the bank and
    robbed us a money bag.
Money is tight around here nowadays.
Tell me about it, said Mildred, *it feels like the dog days.*

Come here Mildred, let's not worry no longer... give your honey bun
    a smooch...
I don't want your smelly kiss now, scooch!
So, there they sat, looking out the window like a bunch of old
    people doing nothing,
Little do you know they're going out tonight clubbing.

In the Act of an Interlude

Nicole Fontes

Not everyone will accomplish everything they wished for,
That's just life.

Not everyone will keep a positive mind-set when they realise
It's not going the way it should and we've been set up to fail,
That's just how it is.

Everyone fakes through all of it, though.
Not because we mean to,
But why intentionally show everyone we're languishing?
That's just what's done.

Eventually we move beyond these thoughts
And persevere with what's left to do before our time is up.
I'm not in a hurry for the clock to stop. But what can you do?
It is what it is.

Roots

Nicole Fontes

I am just like a tree.
I have long, girthy roots.
Some come from the south
Some come from the west.
Every leaf is a moment,
Many have gone, many are now, what's to be?
My tree is constant yet always shifting.
I sway from year to year
Just like the leaves in the wind.
When I'm angry they're sometimes singed.
When I'm happy the tree is in full bloom.
When sad, you'll see me by myself,
On the mountain, accompanied by the moon.

Demons' 101

Kadian Kelly

I'll introduce you to my demons
By their first names,
So, you can know them
As well as I do…

Love,
He pretends to be your friend,
Promises to make you happy
Then takes you by the throat
And sentences you to eternal suffering,
From the inside out.

Conscience
Takes what makes you happy,
What makes you handsome or smart
Then makes you feel ugly, betrayed, unwanted.
Makes you want to hide and cry,
Never show your smile.

They overstay for quite a while,
Make you think it's all worthwhile,
Watch as you're damaged, trying to change,
Laugh at you playing their game that's deranged.

For years and years, I've fought these demons,
Learning every hint and detail.

But they will pay for my soul,
As their death is my goal.

Appearance:
This son of a biscuit
Has a heart so cold,
Makes you want to look like gold,
Gnaws you down to broken bone,
Slowly corrupts your mind to show

The truest of tongues littering lies.
Broken inside, dulling eyes,
Mirrors shatter, anti-snacker,
Sanity snaps, running tracks,
New clothes, hurting most,
Drowning pain, that's his game.

The twins: Hopes and Dreams.
Little devils...
Pierce your skin, watch the blood flow.

They're inside, watch them grow.
They pursue to take you down.
Hide your secrets, preferably now.
They WILL find them, speak them loud,
Gather around a rumourous crowd,
Take everything you wish to be,
Lock it up and hide the key.

Confidence,
Nickname: Pride,
Hides behind his cunning smile.

Sit and observe for a while:
Boosts your energy, pumps your heart
Only to rip it apart
Like an angry, growling shark.
Takes your friends, watches them depart.
House of plastic, new friend's elastic,
Many of these are just like you
Caught in themselves, suffering too.

I Come From

Kadian Kelly

I come from St Ann's:
Running up the streets
Banging on doors
Begging for sweets.

The white bedsheets
Over my head,
Eyes and mouth,

Ripped apart shred by shred.

I come from school,
Difference, a crime.
My beautiful blue hair
Is sadly denied.

I come from the kitchen
A desk white as snow,
Baking cakes
Colours of the rainbow.

I come to the end,
Self-esteem is low.
The darkness takes over,
Nowhere to go.

Ice-cream Sundae

Kadian Kelly

Four weeks and six days ago
The time leading to half six
I sighed, sweet.

Friday night we walked through town.
The frost biting at our fingers.
Me, my mum, my sister
A secret where we were going.

Past Market Square
Where the beach once stood,
Now a desolate wasteland
Lit by the streetlights,

It hit me.
The smell of hot chocolate and golden pancakes.
Like a beacon of joy,
A light in the darkness
The crêpe shop lit up the cold dark night.

I glanced at my mum.
A smile on her face,
'Hot choc, a crêpe and a sundae'.
That word, sundae:
Sweet, cold, relief.

The warmth hugged me
And, like an animation,
My eyes lit up
At the rich, smooth chocolate
Being dribbled over my waffles,
An American diner
The theme of the shop.

We sat down in a little booth,
Black leather lacing the seats.
First my hot chocolate:
Whipped cream spiralled on top.
I took a sip,
Good God it's heaven.
Then my crêpe:
Strawberries and chocolate
Artistically balanced on top,
Sugar sprinkled like snow.
My fork worked like magic,
Clearing the plate in a second.

Finally, my sundae
In its glory:
Toffee ice-cream chocolate brownie,
Vanilla ice-cream and more,
Whipped cream and strawberries
And the golden ingredient,
Caramel sauce.
A little jar to the side
Made me smile, it'll last a while.

My Name Is

Kadian Kelly

My name is strawberry honey, sweet and dripping
My name is white, every colour hidden
My name is Belgium, Russia or France

My name is me, just plain old me
My name is 6: 1 2 3 4 5 6
My name is Kadian, but there is more to me

Delicious

Samantha Kemp

I'm sat here waiting for a delicious delivery, imagining it as it is
    on its way.
Picturing it… as my patience gets thinner and thinner.
A knock on the door and I'm hyper with the smell of succulent
    cheese
In a box, sat in front of me.
As I open it a heatwave hits me, and the smell of cheesy,
    cheesy pizza
Fills the whole room.
I can taste it as I pick up a slice and place it toward my lips.
The crust as thin as it can be.
And then, the taste hits me:
A taste of success that fills my body
And before I know it, the pizza is gone.
Gone, but for the taste of cheese.

I Come From

Samantha Kemp

I come from a family of six siblings
Who annoy me all day every day
With their words and actions.

I come from Nottingham.
A small place, well so people say,
With dangerous things lurking, ready to pounce.

I come from
Tripping over siblings and toys
In a house that isn't that big.
I come from a family who I love to bits,
Even though brothers and sisters misbehave
And do not understand what life's actually about.

I come from school,
A place where I learn new things every day.
As each year passes
My knowledge grows.

I come from the streets with my friends:
Telling each other what we've heard,
Making jokes out of thin air;
And when the streets turn darker, it's time for home.

I Remember

Samantha Kemp

I remember when I was little. I was the crazy kid who annoyed everyone; now I'm the crazy kid who annoys everyone even more.

I remember when I used to be best mates with Nicola. Now we barely speak.

I remember being in my room in the dark. I used to think the toys were hiding people.

I remember the first time I came to this school. I got lost and didn't know what to do. Now I know the school better than my own home.

I remember in Year Seven meeting this teacher who is clearly amazing in every way, now she's one of my favourite teachers and always in my mind.

A Window

Samantha Kemp

Friendship is like a window,
Sometimes you can see right through it.
But secrets appear, and the window is no longer clear.
You can clean windows
But you cannot clean someone's mind,
Unless they open up what's inside.

Pizza

Dominico Leonardi

Pizza,
What a food,
The hot melted cheese,
The spiced tomato sauce.

It's on the side,
Waiting to be eaten.

The next morning
I creep downstairs.
Everyone's asleep.

It's 7am,
The normal time
I wake up.

Watching TV,
Relaxing...
Oh wait,
What did I have for dinner?

Pizza.
What a food,
The hot melted cheese,
The spiced tomato sauce.

Oh yeah,
It's on the side,
Waiting to be eaten.

I walk to the kitchen,
open the box
And it shines at me.

Oh no,
I have to warm it up.
It doesn't matter.

Moments later, it's gone.

Inside the Hive

Dominico Leonardi

Through the window:
The buildings are tall and wide,
The blue sky shines.
I can see the fallen trees,
The bridge connecting the tall buildings,
The classrooms like cells each connected to the other.
It's quiet, as quiet as a hive that has gone to sleep.

Waiting

Dominico Leonardi

Waiting and waiting...
It was getting late.
Waiting and waiting...
It was silence,
Nothing but the sound of mice.
The horror,
Waiting and waiting...

It was midnight.
People don't understand
The killing at times.
Waiting and waiting...

The sense of wonder,
Where is he?
The boring of boredom
Waiting and waiting...
And then
He comes
And the wait ends.

Peace and Horror

Dominico Leonardi

Peace,
The calm and quiet.
Nothing bad,
Just good.
Colour every turn,
Waiting to be discovered.

Oh
Where did she go?
The moon.
Well, she's not here anymore.

Horror.
Nothing good
Just bad.
Grey and black at
Every little turn,
Where did it all go?

Weather

Casey Sims

Swirls of colourful raindrops splattered on my pale face
Reflecting rainbows on the stained-glass of my eyes.
I try to brush it off, but it stays.
Now the water runs down my fingertips,
The cold travelling down my wrist.
I'm drenched. It swallows me up.
Nothing but a puddle to be kicked,
Is it not obvious I'm already down?

The raindrops are tears of nature,
But some are my own.
You're not going to ask me what's
Wrong, not when the raindrops
Are my best disguise.
Swishing swirls of raindrops splattered
On my pale lifeless cheeks.
Not only drenched with the tears of nature
But tears of my own.
Wet, scared and alone,
The forces of nature carry me home.
I'm a soldier fighting forward,
Who's survived the war in her mind.
Brushing off the mud that surrounded her.
I'm alive, happy and warm.

LGBT+

Casey Sims

I remember the first time I experimented with a girl.

I remember how her lips were layered with a sweet strawberry
chapstick,

Hidden beneath a fresh hint of regret that lingers in the morning.

I remember being confused, the sort of confusion when you try
new food

But you're not quite sure if you like it or not.

I remember the hatred I felt for this 'witch' for making me feel
this way,

She put a spell on me, burn her at the stake:

Denial being the 'logical' emotion branded in my genes.

The world changes, cracks and breaks.

I remember how her jeans fitted her so perfectly,

Complimenting every part of her…

No! No, I'm straight. Brussel Sprout can be her name.

I remember how I hit a boy in the eye with a cold, metal and
glass photo frame

Because he called me a 'lesbian'.

I remember when I learnt that being a lesbian wasn't a bad thing

And I was shocked, shocked like when your mother on
Christmas morning

Lets you unwrap that present she swore you weren't going
to get.

I remember when I smelt that girl's sweet-smelling perfume
and fell in love again

Even after I thought I had made myself believe I was
heterosexual. I mean, I do like boys.

I remember how free and complete I felt when I learnt the term
    bisexual, just like when I read
Through the Ladybird book in primary and learnt the word
    'bicycle'
And finally moved on to Level Two reading.
I remember how me and Mum cried when I came out because
    now there were no more secrets.
I remember how the next day I could taste the sensual summer
    breeze
Layered on my tongue and twisted in my hair
And could feel my girlfriend's soft grip on my hand
But this time, in front of my family.

'M' Is for Money

Casey Sims

The media's blown up,
What about this time?
Is Kim Kardashian pregnant again?
Has Donald Trump finally given in?

Twenty chicken nuggets.
Well this is outrageous,
The obesity rates are rising
And you pull this?

Yet soon enough I'm holding a ticket.
You know that ticket they give you?
Turning you from a person to a number.
I'm a statistic, the BBC's next top story.

I sit on a wooden chair
That feels about as sturdy as one of the media's stories,
Inspecting a grease-infested cardboard box
With a yellow & red 'M',
'M' meaning money.

The soggy breadcrumbs brush against my vaselined lips,
Letting the lies slip through my teeth
That tug & pull looking for something deeper.
My tongue tasting the chicken.
Chicken? Or meat from a tube in a breadcrumb disguise?

How would I know?
So many things now wear a disguise, I don't know what's real.

It tastes good.
Inconsistent, of course.
But to be a good liar you've got to remember your story,
And in the end, there's a moment of truth,
Like the true taste of the chicken nugget:
Some were good, some were bad
But it's the worst taste that stays.

My Name Is

Casey Sims

My name is Casey:
A wave travelling free,
No set direction,
Endless routes to escape to
And limited time to choose.

The waves are rushing past,
Beckoning me
To move faster, influencing my choice
To pick whatever's easier,
As droplets of thought
Cascade…
Reminding me of how soon
I'll crash.
Nothing but another grave amongst the many:
My name is Casey.

Azalea

Klaudia Studnicka

Her eyes
Are a completely different world,
An ocean of thoughts and feelings,
Anger, misery, joy.
All mixed into one beautiful being.
Yet, deep under, you'd never know what she truly sees
With those beautiful eyes of hers.
She's like a soldier on a battlefield, standing alone,
Her comrades beaten to the ground.
The phantoms of the past and present, unable to leave,
Unable to enter the Eden they beg to see.
Voices fill the air,
The calls for help only she can hear.
Whispers that sound like thoughts
Maybe I'm mental, insane!
Yet the truth is
This little girl
Has the eyes of a prophet.

Code: Abo-ut.Me

Klaudia Studnicka

It was all so sudden,
One moment I'm behind the wheel
The next I'm flying through the glass
As their car collides with mine.
It was a second. But now here I am.
The new attraction, invention.
The pain long-forgotten as my mechanical heart fuels me,
Each beat so similar to the real one.
Is this how far we have gone?
From a complete wreck of a person, I became this.
Superstar, miracle, a machine with a mind of its own.
My body filled with wires and sensors.
There is so little of the real me inside me.
But the blame is on me.
If I'd only listened, if I'd stayed
Maybe my life wouldn't have ended up this way.
Each day a new code is added,
My hard drive obediently saves it.
If you were ever to take it out
You'd see the memories of a lonely boy,
A devastated mother
And a tragedy
That my eyes have witnessed
And this code has saved.

Redamancy

Klaudia Studnicka

I can't figure out
What it is about him that makes my heart go wild.
Maybe it's his gentle voice:
His loving whispers under the moonlight,
This sensation of delight and safety when I'm in his arms.
Maybe it's those eyes:
That intense gaze, when they look into mine,
This spark they gain when he sees I'm there,
This chemistry is so new yet so wonderful.
Maybe it's those lips
That curve upwards every time he sees me,
The lips I so desperately want to taste.
Maybe it's his personality:
The sweet things he says when we stargaze together,
Or those vows that made me cry with joy.
There is this smile that comes upon my lips whenever I think
of him.
I can see his sparkle of love for me,
And feel the butterflies fluttering inside, desperate to be free.
And there's a loneliness whenever he's not next to me.
This is what love is, isn't it?
You can't quite figure out the reasons you love someone
Because no matter the looks or the age,
You get tangled in their perfect
Imperfections.

My Goosebumps

Kirsty Tracey

I was just sitting there until…
Until I thought somebody was behind me.
I leapt behind myself, up to the window
And through the distance I saw somebody.
It looked like me… I… I was thoughtless,
This person was my shadow!

It didn't seem normal, instead… original.
It wasn't false, in fact it was true:
'My shadow you're possessed!'
'Yes,' said my shadow, 'and so are you.'

Why I Write

Kirsty Tracey

Why do I write?
I write to let people hear what I see.

I write so I can go
to the world of imagination.
Writing is the whispering of whales,
Wondering what's next,
Wondering how to survive
On the wild ride,
That's why I truly write.

Secrets

Kirsty Tracey

The truth about secrets,
The things that make us the way we are
Are our secrets.
The things we keep inside make us special,
Unique and, best of all, ourselves.
Shhh! Your Self
Is a secret.

That Blue Feeling

Kirsty Tracey

There's a feeling that I feel,
To be honest though
Not that often,
It's a feeling that comes and goes.

Lately I've felt it.
I've thought
And thought
Of every colour
I can possibly feel,
But... all I feel is
Blue.

Blue...
It feels like silky warm water
From the inside of my heart.
It's like tears but
This time they fill the room,
Like a tsunami has come.
It's never good to think about
But I can't think of anything else.
So, I ask, *What does blue taste of*?
It tastes of salty water,
Water from the Pacific Ocean
Washed from the storm inside.

Bowling in the Mountains

Alex Vlachou

He wakes up in the mountains, and searches his pockets for his phone but all he finds is the mini bowling set that the old man gave him. Puzzled, he holds it up to the sunlight and says: 'Finally, I understand the purpose of this mini bowling set'. He then eats one of the pieces 'Mmm... chocolates...' he says, and proceeds to eat the entire packet. After a minute or two the voice of the old man echoes in his head, 'You're a laugh but your power of laughter will only be unlocked by something black'. Then his eyes start glowing and an unimaginable pain makes him spew fire and burn the green screen. 'Oops!' Says our hero, running out of the studio.

The Way I Write

Alex Vlachou

The way I write is very messy. It's a weird
Sort of joined-up way of writing
That very few people can read. I sometimes
Can't read what I wrote two or three minutes
After I wrote it. And it would probably happen
If I was reading the written version of this.
I really don't like *how* I write,
But I guess that doesn't matter
As long as I like *what* I write.

A Tree

Alex Vlachou

A tree is constant yet shifting,
A rock is dead yet living,
And the sea is silent yet speaking.
All things around us are quietly sitting, waiting
To be more.
It is at this moment that they'll start screaming.
Maybe for help, maybe for excitement
But one thing is a fact... everything is living.
So just remember that
There is a reason for things existing.
That reason, no one knows,
And if you're desperate to find out
You might as well keep searching.

Friendship Is Almost a Window

Ayah Ali Yousaf-Zai

Friendship is almost a window, through
Which we can see the outside world.
You can clean it, you can decorate it,
But you can't change what it is.
You can't change who it is.
At the end of the day it is still a window
Which you look out of
While telling the same blatant lie:
I'm fine, I have lots of friends,
Then struggling to remember their names.
When you come back home, and your parents ask:
How was school? and you launch into
An utterly fictitious account of your 'friends'.
You carry on looking out the window.
Then one day, no different from the others,
Neighbours move into the house next to yours
And, with a pull and a push,
And a rattling rush,
Their child opens a window.
And now,
Now you have a friend.

Wasted Time

Ayah Ali Yousaf-Zai

As the blue moon booms through the clear window,
As the diamond chandelier hangs dimly on the ceiling,
As relatives cheat and laugh while playing board games,
As the faint buzz of a TV
Can be heard though no one is watching,
Hyper children run around as a person writes.
Probably something incomprehensible and unimportant,
A childish rant, perhaps.
Who would want to waste their time doing that?
But maybe they don't have a choice, for in this endless loop,
As the blue moon booms through the clear window,
Someone is thinking about this right now
And someone is reading about this right now.
As the diamond chandelier hangs dimly on the ceiling
Someone is stopping everyone from having fun.
Who would want to waste their time doing that?
Definitely not me.

Miracle

Ayah Ali Yousaf-Zai

She stared at the sun, blazing with no mercy. She was the only one on the sand, her hair blowing wildly but she stayed focussed as the sun accepted her challenge.

The sun had given her a headache and now she was freezing; her clothes wet from the sea. She was tired. Her feet ached, her head burned, her eyes drooped but she didn't dare blink, she didn't dare sit down, she didn't dare move. If anyone saw, they would say or wonder: *What on earth is she doing?*

Nobody knows what she's doing, why she's here, staring at the sun instead of at the hospital with her family. Nobody knows what she's been through, how it ended up like this. Everybody knows it's crazy, it's impossible! But she thinks that if she stays there long enough, until the sun goes down, she can return and everything will be alright. Of course, it's crazy, impossible! But maybe she knows that too, maybe this is her only shard of hope right now. Maybe you should hold your tongue, if you see her gazing at the sun. Because now the waves die down and the sea stops foaming and the most important thing is, the sun goes down. A single tear streams down her dirty face, leaving a clear mark. And just when she's ready to smash her shard of hope, a phone call sounds. She braces herself, takes a deep breath, ready for impact… but that's not what happens. She screams joyously and runs for the hospital.

Maybe it's a coincidence.

Maybe it's a fluke.

Maybe it's a miracle…

Six-Word Biographies

Chloe Belshaw

Lilly and me once ran away

Kiera Campbell

Hit me with a good book

Kamilė Ćerekavičiūtė

Too many thoughts for six words

Caitlyn Clegg

The sound of pure snow, crunching

Nicole Fontes

Open-minded, diverse, friends of every background

Kadian Kelly

Fun, happy, abnormal, scared – that's me

Samantha Kemp

Weird, annoying, yet wonderful in ways

Dominico Leonardi

The tree that never stops growing

Casey Sims

Forget the phase, you're still gay

Klaudia Studnicka

Oh no! My imagination leaked here!

Kirsty Tracey

Hate fakes, love mates, never late

Alex Vlachou

Depressed little parrot with wonderful life!

Ayah Ali Yousaf-Zai

Holy verse and miracle in Arabic